TRUMPLESTILTSKIN

First published in Great Britain in 2020 by
PICCADILLY PRESS
80–81 Wimpole St, London W1G 9RE
www.piccadillypress.co.uk
Owned by Bonnier Books
Sveavägen 56, Stockholm, Sweden

A CIP catalogue record for this book is available from the British Library.

ISBN: 978-1-80078-004-0

also available as an ebook

1

Printed in Poland

Piccadilly Press is an imprint of Bonnier Books UK
www.bonnierbooks.co.uk

Konnie Huq
& James Kay

TRUMPLESTILTSKIN

Illustrated by
Rikin Parekh

Piccadilly
PRESS

TRUMPLESTILTSKIN

In a faraway land called the United States of Kraziness (or USK for short) there once lived an angry little man with a fuzzy orange hairpiece and a funny orange face.

Although nobody knew his real name, he was nicknamed Trumple. Everyone thought that Trumple had been given his nickname because ever since he was a tiny baby he couldn't stop 'trumping' or breaking wind. He pretty much farted ALL THE TIME. The problem had only worsened as he grew older because of his terrible diet of junk food and fizzy drinks. All the colouring and additives had turned both him and his weird wig bright orange – so much so that he was almost fluorescent.

If there was one thing Trumple loved as much as himself it was gold. As a baby he wore gold nappies, sucked on a gold dummy and rattled a gold rattle whenever he was rattled.

The older he got, the more and more gold he wanted. Oh, and power – he wanted more and more of that too. So as soon as he was old enough he joined the family business, grabbing himself more and more gold and more and more power, until he was completely in charge.

But even that wasn't enough. Nothing was enough for Trumple. Not the skyscrapers he now owned, nor the companies he now ran, nor the hotels and golf courses he had acquired, not even the fact he lived in a giant golden tower called Trumple Tower – oh no . . . none of it was enough – he still wanted more. Trumple wanted to be king!

The USK already had a king who was kind and caring, but Trumple wasn't going to let a silly little detail like that get in his way.

'I want to be king!' he yelled from his golden high chair, throwing a tantrum and throwing the king and his daughter Marla into the palace's deepest dungeon. It was a dark, dingy dungeon, with the tiniest little window so high up that you couldn't even see out of it.

Trumple instantly set about redecorating the palace in his favourite colour. Yes, you guessed it: gold. And not just painted with gold-coloured paint – he wanted the real deal. Everything was to be *pure* gold. He wanted 900 golden mirrors – at least one in every room – so he could look at himself all day long. He wanted to replace his normal-sized hairpiece with the biggest golden hairpiece in the kingdom. He even wanted a golden toilet to trump and do his business on (the toilet variety *and* the striking deals variety).

Before long the kingdom was running out of gold. The goldmines were empty and the people were struggling to keep up with Trumple's increasing demands. Everyone in the kingdom had given him their gold, and they were now poor and hungry and didn't even have proper healthcare. (He had sold off the healthcare system in exchange for yet more gold!) But Trumple wasn't content because the palace still wasn't covered entirely in gold. He banged his tiny hands on his half-gold table in a fit of fury.

'**I want gold everywhere,**' he screamed. '**I want it everywhere – NOW!!!**'

Trumple turned such a luminous shade of tangerine that his advisers had to shield their eyes. Just as he was about to throw all his toys out of the pram, so to speak, one of his terrified aides piped up: 'I think the old king's daughter can spin straw into gold, your royal orange-ness.'

Immediately Trumple ordered Princess Marla to spin all the straw in the kingdom into gold. But Marla was an intelligent and stubborn young girl, and, knowing she could strike a better deal, she refused.

So Trumple made Marla an offer: if she spun ten kilometres of straw into gold, he would give her three chances to guess his real name, and if she guessed it correctly, he would free her and her father from the dungeons.

As it was her only hope, Marla agreed.

She spun and spun and spun until her fingers were red and raw and the entire palace was finally covered in gold. The household was so shiny and blinging that nobody could see where they were going. The servants kept getting dazzled and were constantly bumping into each other.

Meanwhile Marla was at her wits' end: she just couldn't guess Trumple's real name. She'd already had two really good guesses but it turned out that Trumple wasn't actually called Poopoohead or Fartyfartybumpants and now the time was fast approaching for her final guess. Marla's dad, the wise old king, had pondered the problem long and hard and suggested that perhaps Trumple was short for something. But what?

Trumpleton?
Trumplesmith?
Trumplepoopoohead?
Trumplefartyfartybumpants?

It was no use. All was lost. Marla stared forlornly into one of the golden mirrors Trumple had left in the dungeons so he could gaze at himself when he came to taunt the old king. As she watched a tear roll down her cheek, Marla spotted something in the corner of the mirror. Reflected through the bars of her cell window, she could just about make out a huge gold sign being hung by workmen over the palace gates.

'NIKSTLITSELPMURT,' it read.

'Nikstlitselpmurt!' thought Marla, 'could that be Trumple's real name?' It would certainly make sense for a person as self-obsessed as Trumple to have his name emblazoned in gold across the front of his palace. But she had never heard of anybody called Nikstlitselpmurt before.

Marla pondered this strange word for a moment. But only for a moment.

'I've got it!' she cried. 'We're reading the word in a mirror. If you look at any word in a mirror, it will be spelt back to front. All we need to do is read the word backwards! Nikstlitselpmurt backwards is Trumplestiltskin!

Trumplestiltskin, that's his real name!'

Marla and the king hugged each other and cried tears of happiness. They would finally be free!

When they told Trumplestiltskin his name, he was furious. He couldn't believe they had worked it out locked away in the dungeon without newspapers or social media! How had they known? He just couldn't understand it.

'Not fair!' he cried, kicking and screaming
and spilling his milk everywhere.

The orange colour in his face had
reached nuclear levels and it seemed
as though his entire head might explode.

'Nooooooooooooooooooooooo!!!'
he cried as he let out a trump so terrific
that the whole palace shook. It was
the loudest fart Marla had ever heard.
It was so forceful, in fact, that it sent
Trumplestiltskin flying into space –
never to be seen again.

Postscript:

Marla is currently studying International Relations at a world-class university, while her father enjoys a successful career on the after-dinner speaking circuit and has his own TV series on Netflix.